Ben is going shopping.

Stay by me.

Stay by me.

Stay away
from me.

They go into a big shop.

They look at shoes.

They look at bags.

They look at socks
and pants.

Ben sees the toys.

Where is Ben?

They look for him.

Where is Ben?

Where is everyone?

Ben is lost. What will he do now?